PICK of POSY

also by Posy Simmonds

MRS WEBER'S DIARY
TRUE LOVE

Posy Simmonds PICK of POSY

FONTANA/COLLINS

First published in Great Britain
by Jonathan Cape Ltd 1982
First issued by Fontana Paperbacks 1984

Made and printed in Great Britain by
William Collins Sons & Co. Ltd, Glasgow

The drawings in this book have been taken from episodes of
The Silent Three, a weekly cartoon strip appearing in the *Guardian*.

Happy ever After

It is breakfast time at the Webers'....

It's *not* THE wedding dress, silly! It's only an artist's guess....

But it's lovely!

George finds himself one of the carefully selected members of the public to receive a remarkable offer...

Good Grief!

Heirloom Heritage

To celebrate a proud moment of British History *Royston Grange Ltd* proudly present

The Royal Wedding Silver Scoops

A unique silver-plated edition of Metric Measuring Spoons, embellished with the Princely emblem & commemorative inscription.

A handsome, hand-crafted reminder of the part of our National Life which is permanent & long lasting.

Haa haha! Look at *this!* Unbelievable!

Heeheehee! Oh dear! 'Its *own* numbered certificate of authenticity'!... Haha!

This wedding! REALLY!

"Bake your own Royal Wedding cake"

...and that *snuff box!* It's DAFT!!

Oh SHUDDUP Mum! Dad! Stop *spoiling* everything!

You've done nothing but SNEER ever since February!

Yes!

Just because you don't believe in ROMANCE! Just because all your friends are DIVORCED & MARRIED millions of times!

Just 'cos you don't believe in anything *permanent* and *long-lasting*....

I never said...

You're always so CYNICAL! You *can't* believe that *2* people can get MARRIED & go on *fancying* each other & always be PASSIONATELY in LOVE...

For EVER & EVER!

Yes we can! WE'VE been married 19 years & we're still *passionately* in love & fancy each other...

Who? You & Dad?

Yes

What!?

Passion-ately?

Still?

Yes!

God! How GROSS!

7·15
Naturescope
Life with the Lions
A pride of *Serengeti* lions filmed by husband and wife team Naomi and Gordon Thigger.

8·00
Sunday

"....Following the **KILL**, the pride *gorges* itself..... Notice how the lions *shear* off chunks of flesh with their *carnassial teeth*...."

Fortississimo: Crunch! Munch! Gulp! Gollop! Guzzle! Gulp! Snarl! Slurp! Chomp! Gulp!

"Kimba indicates she is in *oestrus* by urinating throughout her territory....."

"Glandular action gives her urine a special *scent*, which tells the **MALE** that she is ready to *mate*...."

"Rajah needs *NO* encouragement... At first, Kimba doesn't welcome his attentions...But *persistence* pays off!"

Sotto voce: Ce programme n'est pas très **SUITABLE** pour les enfants...

Too much ess...ee..ex and vee..eye..oh..el..ee..en...see..ee

"Kimba shows her submission by *squatting*...Rajah then..."

Children, have you fed the guinea pigs?

No, we didn't.

Well, we've had enough **TV** for one evening, haven't we? And it's *school* tomorrow. Go and feed *Keith & Phoebe*.

Ooow

CLICK!

Ooh la la, Keith! Pas devant les enfants!

Keith & Phoebe

BRAN

© Posy Simmonds 1980

...ther ti-ny seeds are called *sperm*. You can on-ly see them un-der-a *mic*...*mickros*.... *mice-rosscope*...*ther*....

Clink clonk!

Tsk! *Who's* knocking the milk bottles over?

Tsk! It's Belinda & Jasper...

ess..en..oh..gee..gee..eye..en..gee.. Oh I *do* wish she *wouldn't* out there! It's *so* *FURTIVE*! It looks so *AWFUL* for the neighbours..... they'll all think we disapprove... she's got a perfectly good room!

Ooh! Are they *MATING*!?

Are they?

Lemme see!

No they are *NOT*! They're just kissing and being *ROMANTIC*... Now, leave them alone.

But *KISSING'S* to do with *MATING*...it says so here! What's *ROMANTIC* mean if it's not to do with *MATING*?

Listen...*ROMANCE* is what happens at the beginning of loving someone...it comes before marriage... and mating....

...like in the *PANTO*...the *Prince* has to say soppy things in the moonlight to Cinderella..remember?

And that's what Belinda & Jasper're doing. *ROMANCE* is saying *lovey-dovey* things, like the Prince did....

Oh Cinderella, your hair is like gold, your skin is like peaches...your eyes are like diamonds...

But what's he say all that *FOR*?

Well.. to make Cinderella feel nice...so that he can get to the real point...which is to *POP* the *QUESTION*.....

Will you marry me?

Please can I post a seed in your tummy?

© Posy Simmonds 1981

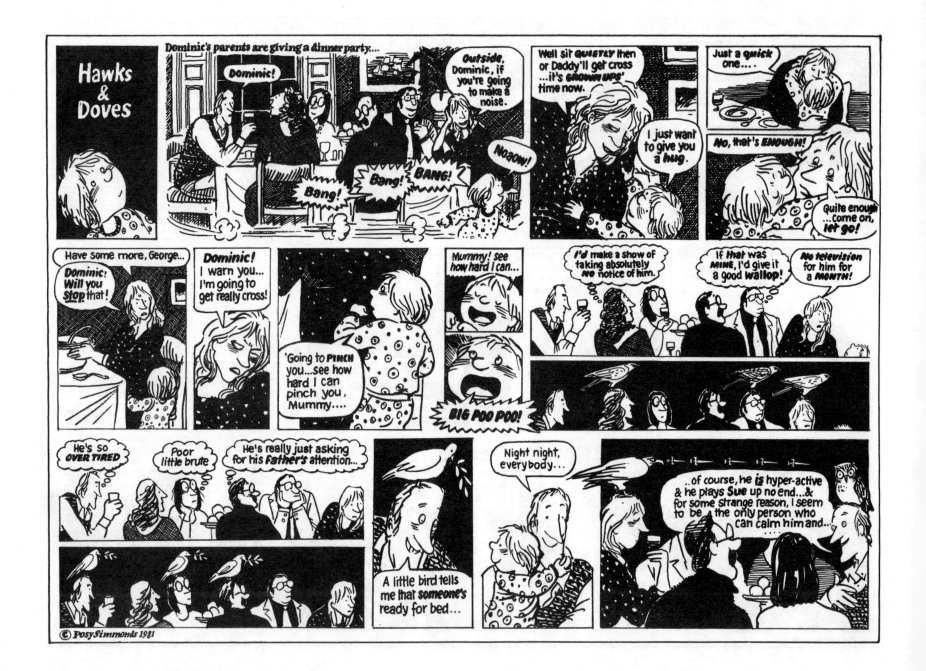

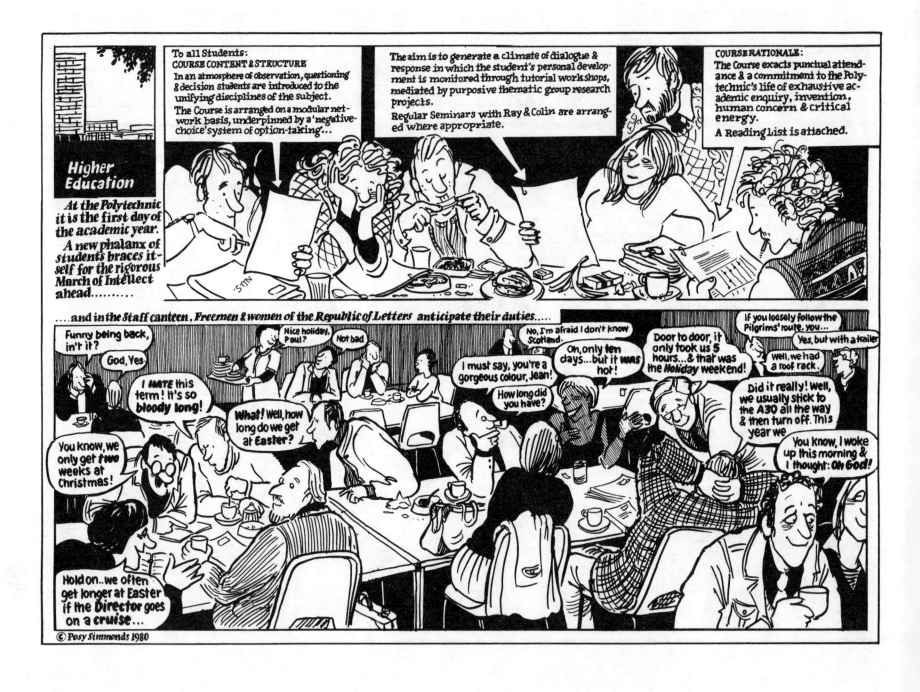

EXCHANGE OF VIEWS

At the Polytechnic, efforts to alter the staff-student ratio have forced the Dean to HACK at the DEAD WOOD in each department.

Today he persuades a member of staff to accept the idea of EARLY RETIREMENT.

© Posy Simmonds 1980

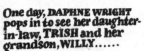

The Silent Three of St Botolph's

Listen with MOTHER·IN·LAW

One day, DAPHNE WRIGHT pops in to see her daughter-in-law, TRISH and her grandson, WILLY......

Hello darlings!

I've just been to a PRIVATE VIEW... gorgeous OILS of African Wildlife...

..& I nearly bought a SWEET old lion... snoozing in a Baobab tree!

And WHO is that little fellow, Trish?

It's WENDY'S youngest – BENJI. I'm looking after him, while she's working today.

POO POO! Hah ha!

WO WO

Oh that POOR Wendy! I always feel SO sorry for her... 6 children! Having to produce ALL those GIRLS before getting THAT ONE. I SUPPOSE he's a CONSOLATION to them, poor souls.

POO POO! he-he-he

Very odd THESE DAYS to wear yourself out having a huge family... Wendy Weber's not a CATHOLIC, is she?

No... thought not.

Still I suppose it's just as well some of OUR SORT propagate, with all the LOWER ORDERS & IMMIGRANTS breeding like FLIES...

And Joanna... how's she? JUST the 3 & all rather plain as I remember...SUCH A SHAME, that weird husband....

That reminds me, here's the address of that nice DOCTOR LECKIE...now you MUST see him, Trish...at your time of life, you can't hang about can you?

Who knows, you may have more than a fence running round your garden next year! AHA!...SUCH A SHAME for you & Stanhope...ONE isn't really a FAMILY, is it?

POO POO!

Look, Daphne...we're not TRYING to have another BABY...we only want ONE child...we're very happy with WILLY....

ONLY ONE! I am SURPRISED!.... I thought you LIKED children, Trish!

I think SOMEONE'S forgotten their manners! SOMEONE'S got to learn that we DON'T LIKE that kind of TALK!

Yes, I think SOMEONE HAS!

BIG BUMMY! POO! He He He!

B

© Posy Simmonds 1978

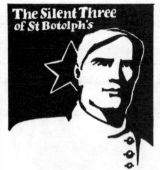

The Silent Three of St Botolph's

THE DENTIST

TRISH WRIGHT has got tooth ache..... As her own dentist is too busy, she manages to get an EMERGENCY APPOINTMENT with CRAIG CROMBIE, an Australian Dental practitioner.....

Here is Trish in Craig Crombie's waiting room:

Mrs Wright?

KARL MARX

N.H.S. DENTAL CHARGES

Please take one

SOCIALIST POST

Punch

UNION SLAPS DOWN CAPITALISM SWEAR

Now, let's look in your DARK INTERIOR, Mrs Wright...

It really is frightfully sweet of you to see me at such short...

Well, we've got a little TROUBLE here...you're very RUN DOWN, aren't you? What you need is a holiday....

Oh, we're supposed to be having one... soon... I mean...

...it's one of the..er PERKS of his job... I don't APPROVE really...um..

..in the..er Virgin Islands ...my husband wants to go...that is...

...I'D rather spend a few days at our... er...COTTAGE...

Nice to have 2 HOMES...

SORRY! Touched a TENDER SPOT did I?

Mmnff!

And what does Mr Wright do?

He's in...er... ADVERTISING

Now, I just want to PROBE that nasty little bit....

My husband makes people want things they don't really need!

And what d'you work at, Mrs Wright?

I don't...I mean..I've got a small BABY

Who's looking after Baby today? Sorry! ...a bit near the nerve...

I have this friend who cleans my house ...NO...NO!...she's..

...REALLY MY DAILY..& she's looking after him!

OK...now, I can't get to the root of the trouble till we've cleaned up the INFECTION with ANTI-BIOTICS

We have 2 CARS.. my husband plays GOLF 2 afternoons a week...our son will have PRIVATE EDU..

So, here's your prescription..they may make you feel DEPRESSED. All righty?

© Posy Simmonds 1977

The Silent Three of St Botolph's

THE DENTIST PART II

WHAT is a nice bourgeois wife & mother like TRISH WRIGHT, doing REVISITING the dental surgery of MARXIST Australian, CRAIG CROMBIE?

Praxis — CAPITALIST CONSPIRACY OF SILENCE!

KARL MARX

I felt so much better after seeing you, last time!

We drained off a lot of POISON, didn't we?

Last time, Trish guiltily volunteered having 2 HOMES, 2 CARS, a DAILY HELP & a husband who plays GOLF in business hours.

Now, I'll just give you a PALPATORY examination.

How's BABY?

My..er...DAILY's looking after him...but I'm going to do without HER soon.....

I don't see why she should do MY chores as well as her own.

Well, this looks TIDIER, Mrs Wright...how's HUBBY?

He's doing a really AWFUL advertising campaign for cruises to SOUTH AFRICA...he's got a MISTRESS.....& he still wants to send our son to PUBLIC SCHOOL.....

Now, this'll HAVE to come out, eventually, you know...

your JAW's too narrow...

I am going to get rid of our 2nd car

Would you chew this little DISCLOSING TABLET? We'll see how clean you are.... PLAQUE 'll show up RED...

You HAVE done well, Mrs Wright! Hardly RED at all!

Oh – is that GOOD? NOT to be RED? That's O.K.?

It's very O.K., Mrs Wright... & you've improved so much since last time, I'm going to give you a BADGE!

A BADGE! *Protanopic Mother Heroine?*

Here you are

I am a good Patient

Keep 'em clean & remember: NO CANTERING around the PADDOCK with your MOUTH OPEN...all righty?

So...I'm STILL a PHAGOCYTE in the BLOODSTREAM of the BODY POLITIC®

© Posy Simmonds 1977

HOME
is where the Heart is

The Wrights & some friends are en route for a convivial weekend at their country cottage....

God, isn't it *wonderful* to get out of all that!

I must say, going to the cottage is the one thing that stops me going completely *BONKERS!*

I *love* that place! I can hardly drag myself away from it...it's where *I* feel I *belong*....

we're very lucky to have it...& it's still relatively *unspoilt*...well, so far.

Is there a lot of local *unemployment*?

Helluva lot...it's *GHASTLY*...about 65% of the *school leavers*, too

Tsk!

...and *wages* way down the *national average*...

...and the *cost of living* is very *steep*...

You pay *Harrods'* prices for most things in our little local shop, Mike.

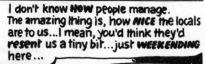

I don't know *HOW* people manage. The amazing thing is, how *NICE* the locals are to us...I mean, you'd think they'd *resent* us a tiny bit...just *WEEKENDING* here...

Mind you, we *DO* take care not to go flashing money about.

They're *MARVELLOUS* people! *Salt of the Earth!* We've really been made to feel *PART of the community*...one gets a *real* sense of *belonging* here...

Well, here we are!

What *gorgeous* honey suckle, Trish!

Ah..*HOME* at last!

Ooh..some *MAIL*...let's see: phone bill...Parish rag...

Oh God! NO!

What is it?

Bloody *JURY SUMMONS!* Would I turn up at Brantwich Crown Court! I'm b******* if I will!

I'm not doing that! Some cases last *ages*...I could be *STUCK* out here for *WEEKS!* ...& Brantwich is such a *one-eyed dump!*

I can't waste time in some *tin pot* court room! ...lot of *bloody YOKELS!* *Sheep stealing*, I'll *BET!*

What a nightmare! ...marooned out here!

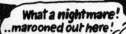

I *told* you not to put us on the *ELECTORAL ROLL* here, Trish...

They don't realise how many *thousands* of pounds of business I'd lose...the *Frostie-Pea* account, for starters...

I must speak to old Aitken when I get back to town... he'll know a *wrinkle*...

Completely *RUINED* my weekend!

ALWAYS WELCOME

When my student *stepdaughter* moved out into **DIGS**, I seem to remember our saying.....

Jocasta, you must feel you can come here whenever you want...

Yes, because it's still your **HOME**.

Feel *free* to come & go as you like.. And your *PRIVATE LIFE's* your private life....we won't **PRY** nor *interfere*.....

So it's *no trouble at all* when she turns up with her boyfriend for supper & a bed for the night.

Hi Trish

Ah, Trisch! How delightful!

Do you like Chinese gooseberries? We brought you some.

Jocasta.. Stefan.. What a surprise!

It's *no trouble* to defrost a little something from the freezer.....it heats in a trice in the *micro-wave.*

What an *enchanting* pie this is, Trisch...

It's *moussaka*.

And it only takes a *second* to put up the *Morphe-Dorm Sleepette*...it's *so easy!*

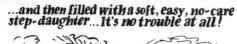

...and it's *so simple* to make....Covered with an *easy-care, no-iron, drip dry fitted sheet* ...& a *light-as-wafer, no-nonsense Drowzy Down* ...

© Posy Simmonds 1980

...and then filled with a soft, easy, no-care step-daughter...It's *no trouble at all!*

GNOSTIC SOUNDINGS
The Journal of Wilhelmine Gnostical Studies

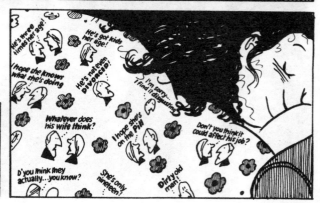

He's three times her age!

He's got kids her age!

I hope she knows what she's doing

He's not even *divorced!*

I'm sorry... I find it disgusting

Whatever does his wife think?

I hope she's on the **Pill**

Don't you think it could affect his job?

D'you think they actually... you know?

She's only nineteen!

Dirty old man!

The Silent Three

A Room of One's Own

PIP PIP PIP
PIP PIP PIP

This is Stefan Torte's answer machine... if you would like to leave a message, please to speak after the *tone*....

☆☆☆☆!

Oh..hello..is that the *babysitter*? um... my *father & stepmother* are out, are they?

They're out to dinner..O.K... thanks. Bye.

SNIFF
SNIFF

O Jocasta! You poor thing... you're DRENCHED!...take off those wet things at once...did you have a TERRIBLE wait AGAIN? Those buses are DREADFUL! Have a nice drink – there's some medium dry in the drawing room.... How was COLLEGE? Did Gilpin like your project? DO hang that up, there's a love... your DAD said he'd be a bit late, so we'll start without, O.K? It's only CASSOULET, so it'll keep...do pop in and say night-night to WILLY... God, Jocasta!–those jeans look a bit LIVED IN.... leave them out tomorrow & I'll shove them in the machine... and YOUR EARS, Jocasta!! Have you looked at them lately?....

CLICK!

© Posy Simmonds 1979

Lonely Heart

Here, amongst the spoils of a happy Christmas, heartbreak lurks:

Dear Marje....
I am 2 Christmases old & my girl friend has left me. I am a rugged, 11½" high Action-Tough-Guy, with moving eyes & gripping hands. One year ago, I met my girl-friend in the Brick Box. It was love at first sight....

She was an 11" high Trudi-Doll, fully poseable, with fashion-hair and lurex Disco-Fever outfit....

"Give us her coat, Benji..."

She loved being dressed & undressed and found real fulfilment in her rôle as plaything.
She lay on top of me for several months...

Then we were moved to the Dolls' House. She knew her place. It was perfect....

...until, suddenly, she began to wear my clothes. It didn't seem right.... she looked hard & unfeminine.

"Now pretend he's the Daddy..."

"Look at her in this, Tammy!"

She borrowed my rifle... there was nothing I could do. She let her appearance go.... her hair was full of Potty Putty.

Finally, last week, she moved into a gyro-powered assault craft, with rotating gun turret.

"She looks ACE in this!"

I have now moved in with a duck. It is not ideal.

"Night, Duck."

My question is, what makes a beautiful doll walk out on a lovely home & manly man? I think Women's Lib has a lot to answer for....

Mrs Johnson's habit of domestic care continues without relief, even at her daughter's home......

Oh Mother! You *shouldn't*! I was going to *shove* it all in my washing machine at the end of the week....

Well, I thought I'd help *relieve* the load... ...I *KNOW* what Christmas holidays are like, dear.

Oh Mum! You shouldn't! Come & sit down..

Now, I'm all right, Wendy, dear... I just thought I'd sort out this little cupboard for you....

You haven't got a *darning mushroom*, have you, darling?

♪ Pom Pom Pom

Oh, you are an angel to do that, Mummy...

THE GUARDIAN

Mother...you *mustn't* miss the end of your serial just because they want to watch this punk rubbish!

But it's *Hugh Janus & the Dropouts*, Mum!

They're *ACE*!

And when the whole house has been scoured & shined, reflecting the glow of each happy heart, it is time to go home....

Let me take that!

Take care, Mum

Thank you so much for a *lovely Christmas*, darling!

Bye, Granny

© Posy Simmonds 1979

S.R.H.

Consumers

...at Ribcock's MAMMOTH carpet event....
.....Broadloom!...SHAG PILE!...tufted Velucrene!!
One hundred miles of CARPET MUST go!!!

:Sigh:

...so, HURRY!! Buy that CARPET NOW! ...& save £££s!!!

BUNTING's Winter Sale starts NOW!

Tsk...as if all that Christmas spending wasn't quite enough

...oh God... our poor, tired media-culture...the Untergang of the Abendlandes....

It's SALE time at Beebat Decor!! This teak-effect lounge unit... ...only £125!! ...This expanded-vinyl suite... ONLY £250!!

LOOK how they emphasise the banality of the object....... EXTRAORDINARY!

...whole lot of reification going on...I mean, it's DREADFUL, but it's WONDERFUL! Such CONVICTION! They don't need their iconography of magic...

FASCINATING! You know Susan Knollys is video-taping this sort of stuff at the Poly, as part of her Communication Design thesis...

RATLINK's Holidays!!! Phone NOW for FREE brochure!!

...'Kleinmeister of the Heuristic Oratorio'....... TERRIFIC!

Oh God, but this ghastly INSATIABILITY

...this...this appeal to ACQUISITIVENESS to solve problems of IDENTITY...so depressing! I mean, it'd make me SCREAM if it wasn't so bloody interesting!

:Sigh: In other words, you're saying we CAN'T afford some new drugget for our back passage.

This is *International Brewhouse Inc's* old corporate identity:

This is their brand new one:

International Brewhouse Inc.

And *this* is the brand new *Regional Office*. Advanced ergonomic thinking & microtechnology have produced the *ideal* in efficient *Workstation* facilities: big thru-put-capacity microfilm installations, new *word processors* & *V.D.U.* consoles, Gastro-mat vending units, *dial-a-matic* telephone extensions with *follow-me* facility...*Everything* to enhance the Organisation's rapid *communications* capability.

© *Posy Simmonds 1980*

And *this* is the *Regional Sales Manager* & some of the *Sales Personnel*, returning from an intensive lunchtime *conference*......

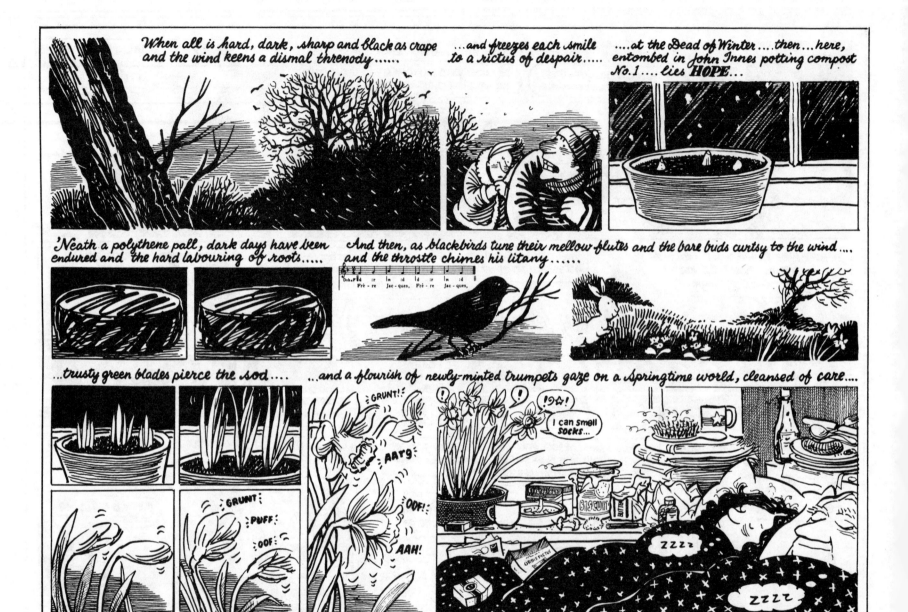

When all is hard, dark, sharp and black as crape and the wind keens a dismal threnody.......

...and freezes each smile to a rictus of despair......

.....at the Dead of Winter....then...here, entombed in John Innes potting compost No.1.....lies **HOPE**...

'Neath a polythene pall, dark days have been endured and the hard labouring of roots.....

And then, as blackbirds tune their mellow flutes and the bare buds curtsy to the wind.... and the throstle chimes his litany.......

Frè - re Jac - ques, Frè - re Jac - ques,

...trusty green blades pierce the sod....

...and a flourish of newly-minted trumpets gaze on a Springtime world, cleansed of care....

GRUNT!

AArg

OOF!

AAH!

GRUNT

PUFF

OOF

I can smell socks...

ZZZZ

ZZZZ

© Posy Simmonds 1981

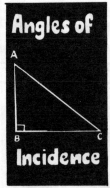

© Posy Simmonds 1980

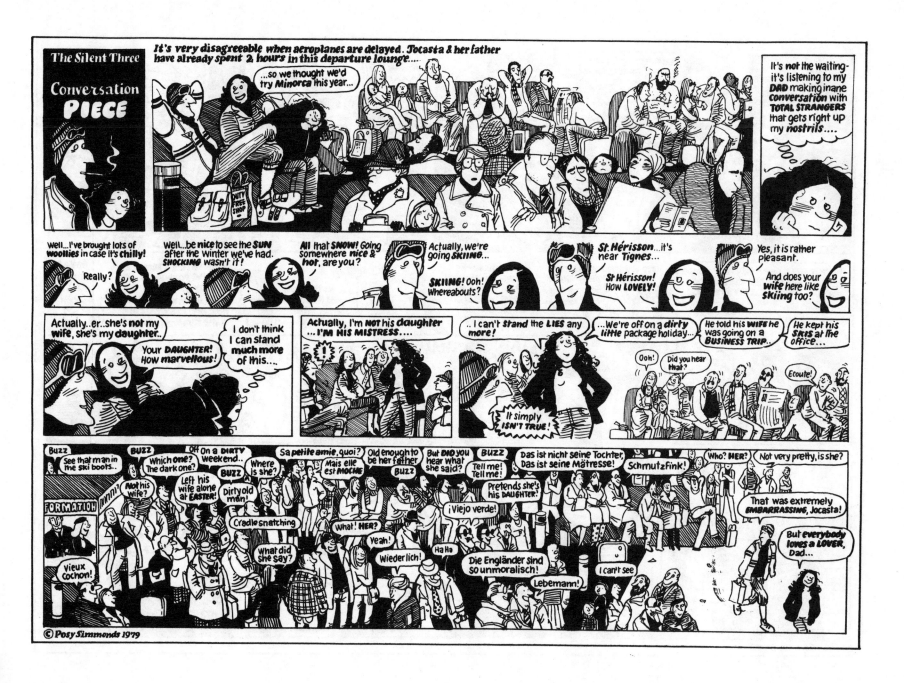

Peaceful Twilight Years

George Weber's Great Aunt Winnie comes to stay....

"Nearly 89." "?" "Sorry, Aunt Win?"

BANG! BANG! Arrgh!

"Nearly 89" "Ah..."

"Poor dear old thing....She's so vague...must be awful to get so old."

"She's all right, Wendy...she's quite happy... cocooned away in her own little world..."

"...she's all very peaceful...gazing at TV all day...not aware of too much...cut off from the hurly-burly"

Police Dragnet Closes in
Vicar in Death Probe

"When you get to that age, you don't take much in...."

Nuclear Arms Race Shock

"Very nearly 89." "?" "Oh I see! No, Aunt Win..... YOU'RE nearly 92...you'll be getting your telegram soon.. Won't that be NICE!"

"What ARE you talking about?" "You said "Nearly 89", & I said...."

"Exactly! Nearly 89 violent TV deaths so far this month ..."The Sweeney," always counts for a lot...."

"They say that today's children see over 10,000 TV murders by the time they're 15..."

"I've seen over 120,000!"

"...And that one doesn't count....it's only a KNEE-CAPPING."

Arrgh!

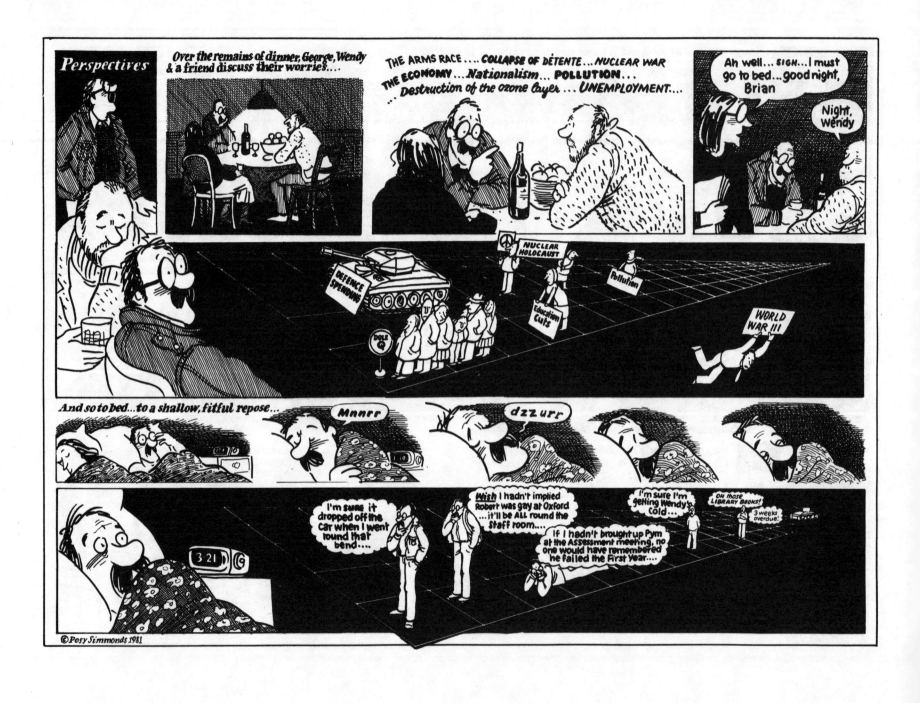

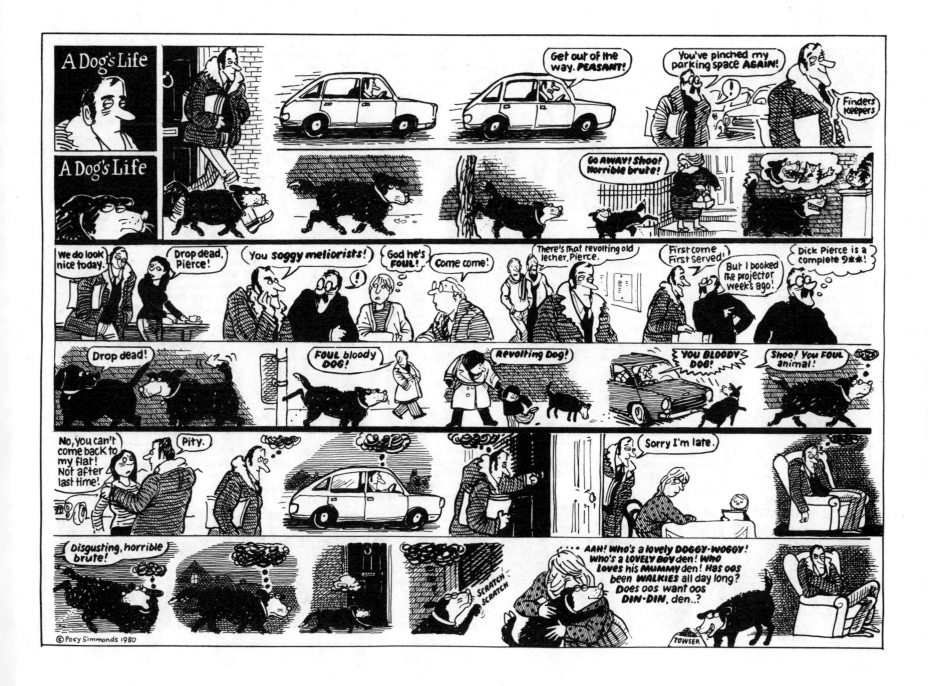

The Silent Three

SHARING

SORRY I'm back so late, Wendy... **SORRY**... ...**sorry**!

Oh dear, you've done the **supper**!

Yes, the kids have had theirs

But it was **MY** turn to do the supper! I really am sorry ...look, **SIT DOWN, SIT DOWN**! Let me get you a drink.. ...will you have **wine**?

Oh **God**, I forgot to buy any!

I've bought some wine

You've been **shopping**? **HELL**! It was **MY** turn to do it.... I just couldn't get to **Sainsbury's** at lunchtime....

And you've **cleaned up**! But it was **MY** turn.... Honestly, Wendy, you might have left the floor for me...

You can do the guinea pigs' cage.

:**SIGH**: I'm sorry... I'm really sorry

Oh, **SIT DOWN** for heaven's sake, George! Stop **apologising**..... You look **done in**...you must have had a **very tiring day** at the **Poly**...

But **YOUR** day is just as **tiring** as **MINE**...the fact that you work at **home** shouldn't mean that you get landed with **MY** share of the **CHORES**!

You shouldn't have done them, Wendy... ...I feel **quite DEPRIVED**!

DEPRIVED?

Yes, **DEPRIVED**... you see, after a **GRINDINGLY HARD** day at the **Poly**... spent discussing teaching cuts in the **Principal's** office, along with his **FOUL pipe**, his **socks** & his **horrible, flatulent DOG**.......

..... after this **AWFUL, TAXING** day, it was **MY TURN** to come home & **shop, cook, clean, cope, iron, MUCK OUT & warm** your slippers!

That's why I feel deprived....it was **MY TURN** to feel really **OPPRESSED**!

© Posy Simmonds 1979

When it is his turn, George Weber goes about the house-work with some vigour...

SCRUB! SCRUB!

POOFF!

! Wha!? Who're YOU?

You rubbed?

D.E.

I am the BON BRUSH TORNADO. I come to reward DRUDGERY, zealously done....

Your wife put in a lot of elbow grease just then... I grant her three WISHES. Where is she? Beating HELL out of the druggets downstairs, perhaps..?

Well, actually, it was ME who did the RUBBING..

Pardon?

You see my wife's OUT at the moment...

OUT? She's no business being OUT! D'you mean to say she's left YOU to do HER job?

Well, I don't mind..she's gone to a lecture..she's a MATURE student...& it's my day to look after the house..., & the kids, of course...

Wicked, selfish WOMAN! Why is she not here? Why is she not on her hands & knees deodorising her home! How can she let her husband fawn all over the bathroom suite!?

A WOMAN's place is in the HOME, you know...they really don't LIKE it outside, whatever people say... ..you see, they're GIVERS not TAKERS ..& they really must be allowed to do the caring

! Floosh!

Floosh Floosh O.K....if that's the way you want it.... whoosh ...but I warn you, I lay this HEAVY SPELL on wives who exempt themselves from their proper duties... May your wife WORRY as she WORKS! May she SUFFER as she STUDIES!

Will George remember Benji's medicine? Oh God! Sophie's piano lesson! Did I get more Hoover bags?.....

ZANOTTI'S
MASTERPIECE

IL
FONDO
XX

WITH
GIULIA DE SENA

It's a shame to waste a babysitter when guests cancel at the last minute, so George & Wendy go to the cinema:

...un corpo come acciaio...

"Yes...I know."

Well, this is all rather tedious...

God..don't know HOW she could go to bed with HIM! Reminds me of Roger next-door.

Hm...don't Italian men have tiny feet!

He smokes rather a lot!

Those sheets are very like the ones we saw in Bivouac...

...only the stripes went the other way.

We do need some new sheets— we must have had ours since we got married...

My God, Giulia De Sena, she's...good grief! ≥ BOGGLE! ≤

I don't believe it! She CAN'T!

My God! She IS!

Bloody Hell!

PWOOOOOOH!!

Rude!

It is quite appalling! Horribly SEXIST...

..revolting SEXIST! It's the most disgustingly revolting, SEXIST thing I've ever seen!

It's the most appallingly revolting, disgustingly SEXIST & EXPLOITATIVE film I've ever seen.

FINE
(THE END)

So glad we agree, George

© Posy Simmonds 1980

© Posy Simmonds 1980

The Silent Three

Uneasy Riders

Currently, Belinda Weber & her boyfriend, Jasper Lushington-Rudd (a *motor cycle messenger*), do not care for Culture, Sexual Equality or Conservation.....

Well, I don't give a *monkey's* about *Balaclava Terrace*, Dad.

SAVE BALACLAVA TERRACE APPEAL FUND

JUMBLE SALE

2·00

ALL JUMBLE TO MRS WEBER

They should go ahead and bulldoze the bloody lot..

You wouldn't think those two had 19 'O' levels between them

VRROOM VRUM

BAT DESPATCH

I suppose they feel they must look like *REBELS*.... I wonder why *motor bikes* are always associated with *SELF ASSERTION*...

Jasper & Belinda aren't *REBELLING*.... they're *CONFORMING*...the *bike* comes with Jasper's *JOB*...& she's a *PASSIVE SEX OBJECT* on the *PILLION*...

..and the law sees to it that their *SNEERS* are hidden under *CRASH HELMETS*...they've just joined their *CONSUMER GROUP*.....

JUMBLE FOR MRS WEBER

Give me the *real* images of *REBELLION*...the *Echt contestations!*

The 1950's...BRANDO in *The Wild One*...

...the 1960's.... *Easy Rider*....

...*Brigitte Bardot*....

...*T.E. LAWRENCE* going to *Clouds Hill*... ...er...*AUDREY HEPBURN* in *Roman Holiday*...

...And *US*, George! *WE* rebelled!...remember in London going on my *scooter* to the *PARTISAN*...and afterwards to the *Royal Court*, to see *something* by *Henry Chapman*!

FUTTA FUTTA

Ah...Heady Days!

© Posy Simmonds 1979

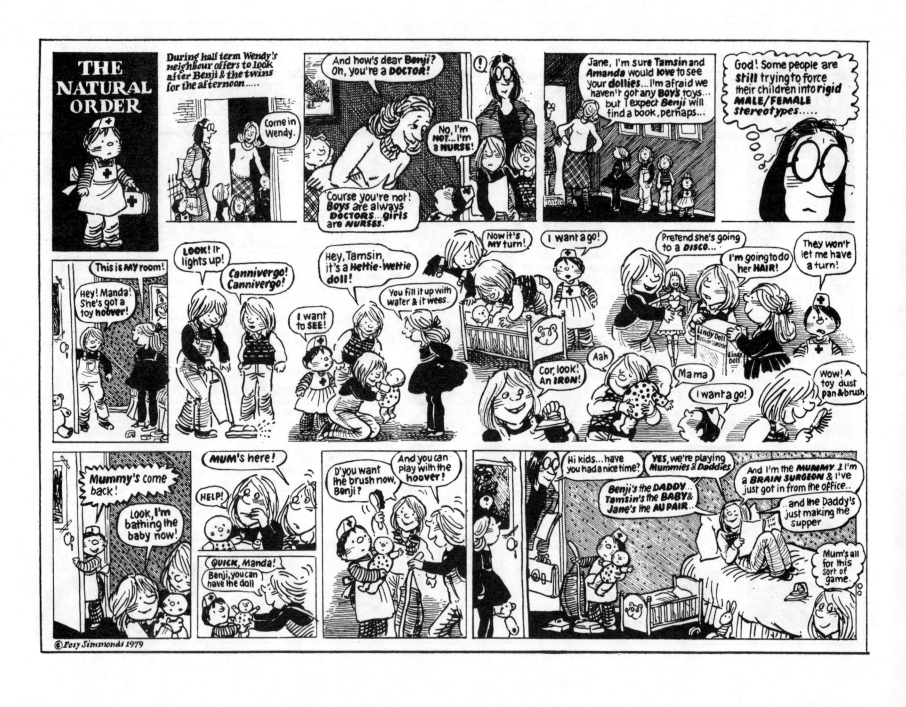

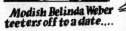

Daily Dose

Jocasta Wright is on her way to art college....

© Posy Simmonds 1981

The Silent Three

Promises, Promises

Must show you the photos of *Sue's* wedding, Wendy....

That's my **EX**: *Sue's father*... you never met him, did you? *That's* his **3rd** wife, Elsa... those are his *stepdaughters*

And that's **ME** with Dan...& Dan's son from his first marriage....

That's *Lizzie* looking like a good time had by all...she's getting married again, you know

...and that's my sister... **SHE'S** got **6** kids now, can you believe it!.....**3** of *hers*, **2** *stepchildren* and now she & Paul have had a joint baby...

That's the bridegroom's stepfather...Alex...

He's a **saucy** old boy...terrible one for the *ladies!*

And here's the bride & groom... *Michael & Sue*.....Oh dear, it's very **SAD** her marrying so **YOUNG**....

Oh, I don't know...I'm sure it's *just a PHASE* she's going through...

The Silent Three

L'Après-Midi d'une Divorcée

Barnaby, Dorcas...get your rucksacks..**Daddy'll** be here in a minute...

Now I'm going to be really **calm** & in control this time... very **DIRECT**...**OUT FRONT**... no **grovelling** or pleading...

"Derek, as I'm between jobs at the moment, I'm a bit **hard up**..... ...could you possibly..."

"Derek, I need an increase in the **children's maintenance**...."

When's Dad coming?

"Derek, the **kids** need **winter coats** & I can't manage the **rates**"

He's **LATE**

"Derek, the kids simply can't **exist** on the **pittance**..."

My **GOD!** He's ½ an hour **LATE!**...if he thinks **I'm** hanging around all bloody afternoon...!!

Derek! D'you know how much it costs me to run that bloody **CAR?**

Bang Bang!

I **hate** him! It's only **one** week end a month..he could at least be **on time**..probably had a **lie-in** all morning.... **WHEN** did I last have one?!! **MEAN ***9!**!**

I hope that **Fat cow Carla** gives him a really hard time...my God he deserves it! **Selfish PIG!**

Poor little kids waiting...he doesn't **care**... doesn't **deserve** to see them..an **HOUR** late! I'll make him pay for this..!!

Dad's here!

Your money or your life, Daddy!

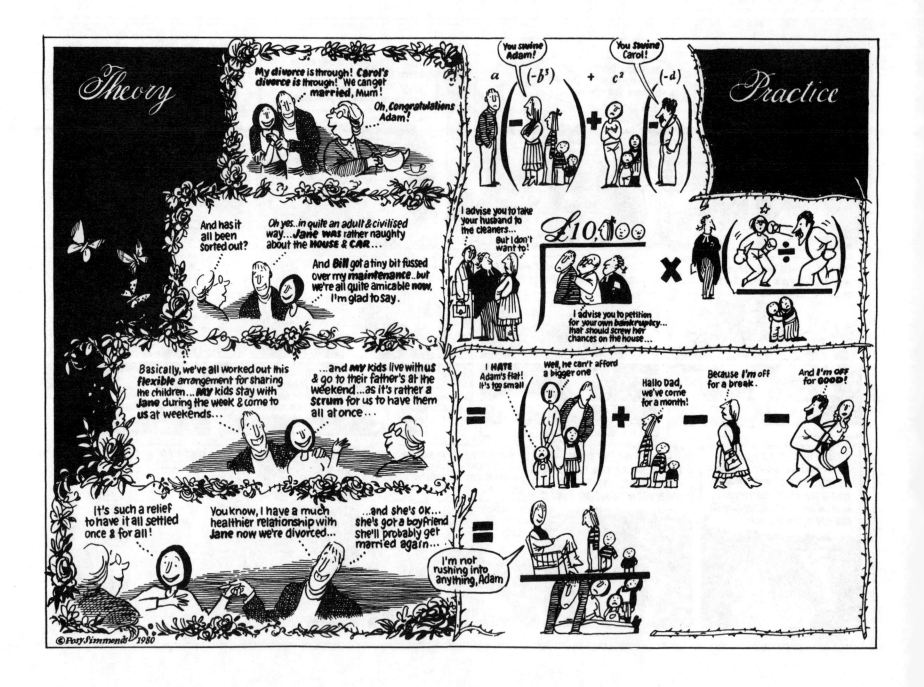

How the Other Half Lives

A divorced woman rings her ex-spouse:

Perhaps you could spare some time to see the children on Saturday.... I want to go out.

THINKS

Well, it's all right for HIM...he's got a very cushy number....he's not lonely....he's got :
1. GIRL FRIENDS. 2. MONEY 3. A BACHELOR FLAT. 4. NO HOUSEWORK. 5. FREEDOM. 6. UNINTERRUPTED NIGHTS. 7. PARENTAL POWER WITHOUT RESPONSIBILITY. 8. NO ONE TO THINK ABOUT EXCEPT HIMSELF.

HE HAS, OF COURSE TO PAY MY MAINTENANCE, AND THAT HE MAKES INTO AN ACT OF CHARITY.

Expensive Modes

Why do you always sound SO ANGRY?

Persil

THINKS

It's all right for HER...she's got a cushy one...........I knacker myself at my job to keep her nice and warm in my HOUSE, WITH MY KIDS AND MY DOG AND MY HI-FI AND MY CAR AND MY DAVID HOCKNEY PRINT...AND I DON'T GET ANY THANKS.

© Posy Simmonds 1981

GOING SOLO

No. 6
Holmleigh

This is Ellen, creator of hand-crafted, wooden house signs... whose husband has recently left her....

Ring Ring!

Hello...

Hi, Ellen, it's *Wendy*... I was just ringing to see how you are

You're *OK?* ...and you're not feeling *lonely?*

LONELY! You're *JOKING*, Wendy! I'm so *happy* about *John* going, you know....

You don't mind being on your own?

No No... I really *welcome* alone-ness, you know, as an emotion *really* worth experiencing...

You know I was feeling a lot of you know... *HOSTILITY*... and I feel I really need to be in my *own space* ..uh.. this flat has become... a kind of *extension* of my whole *selfhood*, you know...

I really *NEED* to be on my own... I mean, when *John* came back to collect his *Hi Fi*, I felt this *total violation* of my *space*, you know... it was *weird*..

But you know, now I just feel the *rightness* of being totally *selfish*... I feel a lot of *JOY*... a lot of *INNER GROWTH* ....

I feel you know sort of really in *touch* with all the *waves* my life creates

Yes, I *know* I could go out and meet *other men* again and *tra-la-la*... but I just don't need that any more... you know, it always ends up with some bloke running your life....

I like being *ALONE!* I live very simply... I *eat* at my *desk*... I *sharpen* my *pencils* into the *tea pot*... I *love* it!

Good good I'm glad..

I'm really *happy*... I feel incredibly strong & *POSITIVE*..anyway, thanks for ringing.

Waaaaa!

Waaow -oow

The Silent Three

Putting the Bootee in

In the course of conversation, Nigel, a married man with two children, deduces that Avril, an unmarried woman, earns three times his income....

...their economy must grow by 2·2% -so my American colleagues say..why are you *STARING*?

I was just thinking... aren't your *EYES* the most incredible green!

But you *are* a *CLEVER GIRL*! You don't look *OLD* enough to be a *Managing Director* -sorry! Direct*ress*!

You're *much too PRETTY* to be involved in *BIG BUSINESS*! What's it like working in a *Man's World*?

THINKS GROAN!

I've no idea

So..what happens when *Mr Right* comes along & sweeps you off to his castle? Eh?

Will you still be Managing Director?

You'd make a wonderful *MOTHER*...intelligent girls like you should have lots & lots of *babies*!

Having *KIDS* changed my life! When you've got *RESPONSIBILITIES*, there's a reason for working hard... otherwise, one just earns *MONEY* for its own sake, don't you think?

Nigel!

My children are my *whole life*! I saw *both* my sons born.... *EXTRAORDINARY* experience!

You mustn't miss out on it!

There's something fabulous about a *PREGNANT LADY* ..a lovely *INNER GLOW*.....

Sorry to interrupt...but we must GO, Nigel...the *BABYSITTER*...

Byee!

I do hope we'll meet again...

Honestly, Jane, the babysitter could have hung on another hour...I was enjoying myself

Attractive girl, that Avril... *INTELLIGENT*..

Y'know...I really admire women like that, who make something of their lives...

GROAN!

≳SIGH≲ I suppose the kids'll wake up at some Godawful hour...

Rich Desserts

Oh, she's *Gorgeous,* Christine!

Adorable! Aaah!

Come here and talk to me, *my Boofuls!*

Is ooz pritty den?

Is ooz lovely ickle baba den?

Has ooz got ooz toofy pegs yet? No? No toofy pegs?

Has ooz had ooz nice din dins den? Ooz had ooz nice num nums?

Nice num nums!

Good ickle baba eat ooz num nums all up! Aaaah!

& is ooz going to bye byes in baba's bassinet?

glerc..

Oh God!

MOTHER KNOWS BEST

Trish Wright has agreed to meet her *mother-in-law* for tea & Danish pastries:

I'm so glad you could *spare* the time, Trish...I want to have a little word with you...

Now, it must be *very* nice for you to be *WORKING* again, but I don't know *HOW* you can leave *poor little Willy* with a *CHILDMINDER!*

One hears such *GHASTLY* stories....*freezing garages* full of *toddlers LASHED* to their *push chairs!*

Daphne, one of my *FRIENDS* looks after Willy ..along with one or two other children...*SHE* adores children...*THEY* adore *HER!*

And Willy *LOVES* going.... he *hates* it when I come to pick him up...& he's *learned* so much there!

Yes, well he's certainly learned a very *COMMON* accent.

Anyway, I still don't think it's right...*I really don't think people should have children if they aren't prepared to look after them.*

Too many of you *girls* these days want to have your cake & *EAT* it! You all *RUSH OUT* to work & then wonder why your children grow up into *MUGGERS*

One just *can't* treat *CHILD-REARING* as a *HOBBY*...

But Daphne..

Now I *KNOW* there are some *poor souls* who are *OBLIGED* to go out to work...& *of course*, I accept that.

Take your dear husband...I mean, when *Stanhope* was *TINY*, I can't *remember* a time when we were *EVER* apart....You see, it was a *PRIVILEGE* to look after him!

He was *SO ADORABLE!* I couldn't *BEAR* to let him out of my *sight!* Stanhope went *everywhere* with me!

Yes..with you *AND* the *Nanny*...

You see, Trish, it's *SUCH* an *important* time when they're *little*...& the *LEAST* a mother can do is to give her *CONSTANT PRESENCE & ATTENTION* to *ALL* her *tiny one's* needs...

Maaaa!

Oh NO! REALLY!...In *PUBLIC!* Oh I *DO* think that's a *BIT* disgusting! Tsk!

Whatever NEXT! Really!

© *Posy Simmonds* 1979

© Posy Simmonds 1979

Parents arrive to collect their children from Tobit's fourth birthday party.....

© Posy Simmonds 1981

The Silent Three

TRÈS SNUB

Here is a drinks party in *full cry* on the patio of Mrs Brinsley Bowe's *bijou res.*

Gay lanterns illuminate a scene where the *kaftan* vies with the *pelargonium*...a *RIOT* of colour!

George & Wendy Weber feel somewhat out of place.....

I don't think I can stand this, George...I don't know anyone... ...I don't *WANT* to know anyone

WENDY! Haven't seen *you* in *YONKS!* How *SUPER* of you to come to my *COCKERS P!*

Brinsley, remember *Wendy*...at school with me? *This* is George....George is something *frightfully CLEVER*...a professor, aren't you?

..er..no..I mean I *AM* a lecturer at a *Polytechnic*

Really? How *RIVETING.*

Awful snobs! They make me livid!

Of course the *hice* will corst *thiysands* of *pynds* to bring up to *scretch*

Aren't your roses absolutely *DIVINE!*

...you'll be able to look me up in *WHO'S WHO* next year.....

I got a *Lancia* out of the Company - they offered me a *JAG* first...

Really! You'll be *bucking* for a *K.B.E* next...

Guess who I saw in the Royal Enclosure?

GULP GULP

Let's go

Wait, Wendy...have another *drink*...I find it extraordinarily interesting *FIELD WORK*....

© *Posy Simmonds 1979*

Such a proliferation of *MOIETIES*—with a common collective mythology, but limited *reciprocity*—presents us with a *discourse* of *TOTEMIC BRICOLAGE*....

GLUG!

I hadn't properly understood the *logical axēs* of our culture..in more than one dimension...

..How we are, ourselves, an *exogamous PARADIGM!*

It's no good, George...if you can't *BEAT* 'em ...*JOIN* 'em!

Brinsley! *AREN'T* your *SOCIAL CLIMBERS* absolutely *marvellous* for the time of year!

AN ACID EXPERIENCE

American *ethno-botanist*, Frisbee Summers, is staying with his old friends, George & Wendy Weber......

GREAT to see ya, Wendy!

After supper, *sulky* Belinda Weber & her boyfriend excuse themselves:

I thought we agreed that you'd *stay in* tonight, Belinda...

Tsk! You'll *never* get to *UNIVERSITY* this way..... ...*DISCOS* every night.

I don't care.

STUFF university! Stuff *EVERYTHING!*

Don't be *SO RUDE!* You *know* you really *must* stay in...... I *insist!*

Hey, that's a really *heavy trip* to lay on them, Wendy. That's not *cool.*

LIFE IS A SEXUALLY TRANSMITTED DISEASE

They're *KIDS*...Remember how it was for *US?* They're *angry* & *horny,* just like *we* were!

...I mean, they gotta *fight* the *SYSTEM,* just like *WE* did, right?

And the *SYSTEM* still *STINKS...* still a *HYPE....*

...like, nothin's changed...*EXCEPT:* *WE* really understand *YOUR* scene, Linda... *OUR* parents sure as *hell* didn't understand *OURS*...but your generation's *lucky— WE* know where you're at...

...because we've been through all those *BAD TRIPS* too, man...

...getting *laid*... getting *busted*... *downers* with the *FUZZ*...

I mean...we've all tried to *FLY* from upstairs windows... *WE KNOW* those really *GRIEFY* scenes, man!

LIFE!

...& like, we've *head-loaded* our kids with our *good-Karma* dreams.....& you know what really *turns me ON?* You're all *SO BEAUTIFUL!* ...it really *blows* my mind!

Like, there're no *barricades* between your generation & *OURS*... we're all on the same *MIND-TRIP!* We're all dreaming of the *BEAUTIFUL SOCIETY,* right? *REVOLUTIONARY TOGETHERNESS* LOVE! PEACE!

KILL!

Jeez man! I love *YOU!* *PEACE 'n' LOVE...* WOW! How 'bout that, hey!

KILL!

© Posy Simmonds 1980

© Posy Simmonds 1980

Pupa Power

But *DID* you see the way it was reported!? Talk about *SEXISM!*

¡Sexism, Sexism! That's all they talk about!

Cobblers, Mum!

Just take yourselves *OFF*, Adam...Lucy...I'm *sick* of your *stupid remarks!* Go on, *GO AWAY!*

God! Honestly! *TEENAGERS!* Mine are a real *PAIN* at the moment, Wendy....

I know the feeling, Kate

I mean, it's always a gamble how one's children emerge from the *CHRYSALIS* of *ADOLESCENCE*... but when I *THINK* of the *HOURS* I spent in the past feeding my little *larvae CULTURE*....

...all those *PIANO* lessons, *BALLET* classes... *KARATE*...*VERSE SPEAKING*, Drama... concerts, recitals, art exhibitions... tennis coaching... holidays in *FRANCE*....

Now eat up that nice *Mondrian*, Adam...

Culture

God knows, I've tried to equip them with the necessary *SOCIAL AILERONS*

Understanding the Problems of: WOMEN, BLACKS, GAYS, The Old, Animals

Qualifications: O Level Maths, O Level Art, O Level Eng, O Level French, O Level History, O Level Physics, O Level Chem

Piano, Jewelcraft, Finger Painting, Karate, Macramé, Simple Joinery, Hygiene, Generosity, Discernment, Fairness, Sensitivity, Tolerance, Social Conscience, Tact

But despite all my efforts, *Adam & Lucy* have turned out *intolerant, insensitive, unimaginative, uninvolved & totally UNCREATIVE!*

...now I realise that all I've raised is *two SLUGS*...who lie about *chewing holes* in all I stand for

I've had a bellyful of these *restrained little FLOWER PRINTS*

MUNCH MUNCH!

Don't they make you want to *throw up?*

CHOMP CHOMP!

Dunno, they're quite *GOOD TASTE*, really.

© Posy Simmonds 1979

Jocasta Wright & her fellow art students are out for a day's *plein air sketching.*

The tutors, faced with the end of another academic year, exchange views of differing dismay.....

God! I hate this time of year...no sooner have you got used to one group, than they're off.. having *worn* you out... *GROAN!*

Roll on *July*...can't wait to be shot of this lot....

Look at 'em! *Depressing* isn't it!

At *least* when I was a *student,* I was *INTO* something!

Today, they don't *care* about *ANYTHING..* they certainly don't care about *ART...* they're so *bored...* all *dead* from the hair downwards.

...& they're *incredibly APATHETIC* .. I mean, *what IS* happening?! There's something very *weird* with kids today...

Yes..a sort of *horrible diffidence* ....an *insensitivity*...

Hey, who you calling *insensitive,* Vic?

You, actually. I mean, take your *T shirt* – those **S**'s are like *Nazi insignia..* ..I find that really *OBSCENE*

And *yours* isn't much better, Jocasta. I don't know how you can wear it!

Oops! Sorry you don't get the *irony.* I'll take it off.

KEEP DEATH OFF THE ROAD... DRIVE ON THE PAVEMENT

No No! Don't be *silly!*

Goodness! The *scales* have fallen from my eyes.. I can't wear these either : *MADE IN SOUTH AFRICA!*

..and *these!* Made in a *Latin American Military Dictatorship!*

For God's SAKE!

KISS

And *THESE! MULTI-NATIONAL-IMPORTED-MAN-MADE FIBRE!* Putting half *Lancashire* out of work!

For God's sake put your clothes on, Jocasta!

You don't mean it, Jocasta..this is all just a *POSE* to you, isn't it?

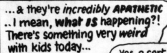

© Posy Simmonds 1980

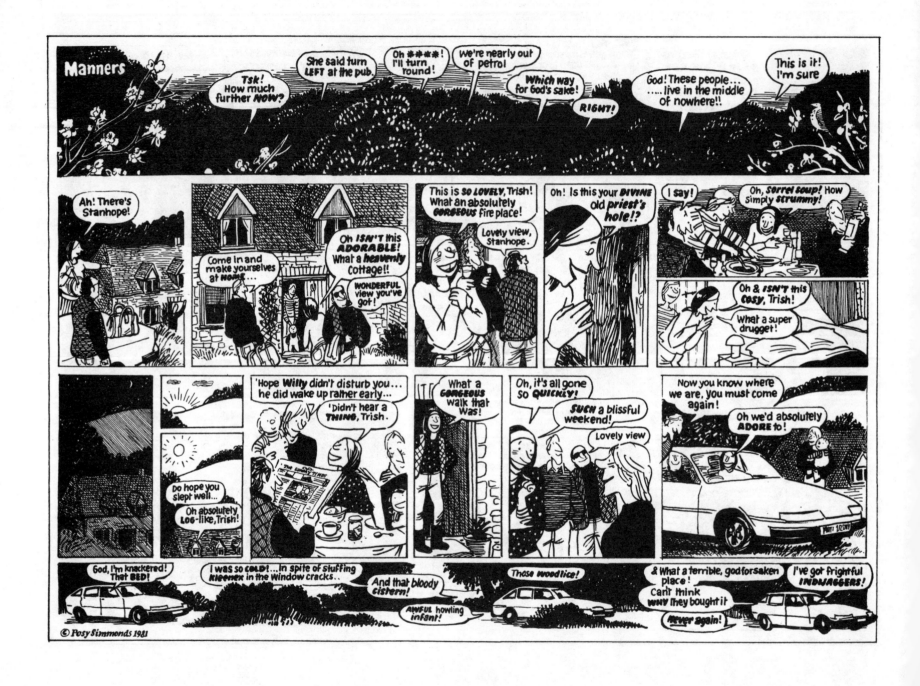

Loss & Profit

PUSSY LITTER

BENJAMIN! What have you done with the CAR KEYS?!!

How many times have I got to tell you....

LEAVE KEYS ALONE!

Didn't

Come on...where did you put them? I'm going to get really angry!

Didn't

BENJAMIN!

George...don't frighten him.

Well, I've had enough! He's a bloody nuisance with keys... I found the MORTICE down the lavatory yesterday

He's got to learn.

Benji...where did you put the keys, darling? Tell me...... I won't be cross...

! SOB ! I didn't!

But you did take them, didn't you?

No!

Well, I think you did darling... just tell me where you put them ...& then we'll go & read a story, eh?

I didn't take them...

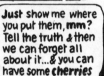

Just show me where you put them, mm? Tell the truth & then we can forget all about it...& you can have some cherries

Did you put them down the loo again? No one's going to be cross if you tell the truth, Benji... You did take them, didn't you?

No!

Just think...you can have some cherries and a story & stay up a bit late...you see, it's very important not to tell lies...You did take them, didn't you?

Yes

And where did you put them?

In Pussy's Corner..

GOOD BOY, Benji!

KISS

?

Moral: Mysteriously, crime often pays.

The Silent Three

L'Étranger

A holiday in France: The Webers pick their way over the exquisite parquetry of bronzed flesh which carpets the sand.... eager to *fuse* with the ambience ....to vault the barriers of language... and to join in the *shuttle cock & battledore* of cultural exchange.......

George, I don't think I *DARE* take *mine* off after yesterday...

Me too, I'm afraid.

Attends un petit moment, Françine!

But d'you think it's *OK* to be *like this*? I don't want to offend anyone....

Relax, Wendy.. anything goes on this beach...

I can feel them all *STARING* ...it's *SO* embarrassing!

Oh dear!

NO ONE'S staring! Honestly, it *DOESN'T MATTER* — we're all made the same!

But I do feel we ought to *SAY* something...... *EXPLAIN*...you know...

All right All right!

PLAGE RESERVÉE AU NUDISME

..er.. pardon... nous sommes obligés de cacher nos *parties privées*...er... *NON* parce que nous sommes *embarrassés*..... mais parce que nous étions *brûlés* là hier par le soleil...✱

© Posy Simmonds 1979

✱ *We are obliged to cover our private parts, NOT because we are embarrassed, but because we were burnt by the sun there yesterday.*

All Good Gifts around us.

Well, Christopher?

The time of *Harvest Fayre* approaches. The curate has been soliciting contributions from the Urban Village Folk...

A bit thin, vicar... the **middle class** lot have responded most... they all look embarrassed & apologise for not being **CHURCH GOERS**... then they make up for it by being generous....

..they're giving lots of produce... I find that reassuring, don't you? I mean, take the **Webers**... I've just had a long, jolly interesting talk with Mr Weber about **Christ's divinity**.....

...and you know, I **WARMED** very much to his testimony..

Are we getting any **FRESH** produce, Christopher... ...for the **church**?

Well... **fresh**-ish

Candida Best's giving us lots of things they've brought back from their **farm** in the *Périgord*... you know, **OLIVES** & **FIGS** & strings of **GARLIC**...she said she'd arrange them on little **nests** of **VINE TWIGS**

She also offered to **strip** the varnish off our **PEWS**.... you should see the *bureau-bookcase* she's just done!

Bother the **Périgord**! Won't we get any **LOCAL** vegetables... off the allotments?

Well... **local**-ish...the Burkes have promised to bring some **runner beans & tomatoes** back from their weekend cottage.

ST LUKE'S ROAD

ST LUKE'S CHURCH
ALL ARE WELCOME

...& I **think** the Fairfaxes have grown a **marrow** on their **patio**...

Not much of a **HARVEST** then...

ST LUKE'S CONFIRMATION WORKSHOP

Oh, but **YES**! As I said, the middle class lot found they could spare some **WONDERFUL** things! Blackberry & apple... **Mealie** bread... **Flans**...

Oh.. that sounds better. Well, it's very good of them to go to all that trouble.

Oh, it's **NO** trouble...it's all out of their **FREEZERS**! It's wonderful what they can store in them!

It'll be like a blooming *Tupperware* party...

"...heapeth up riches and knoweth not who shall gather them..."
(Psalms 39:4)

ⒶMrs Weber's blackberry & apple '79. ⒷMr Burke's Salami Flan 1980. ⒸMrs Fairfax's Carrot Cake '79. ⒹMrs Weber's Mealie Bread (Feb.'80) ⒺMs Pottinger's Sour Cream Pumpkin Pie '80. ⒻMs Evans' spinach purée '78. ⒼMs Evans' soya bean casserole '77. ⒽMs Evans' Goat Curd Cheese cake 1980. ⒾIllegible 1979. ⒿMr Downing's Irish Brack 1979. ⓀMrs Bolton's Crème de Menthe Mousse '78. Mr Weber's Wine Sorbet Ⓛ......

© Posy Simmonds 1980

The Silent Three

The Last Days of Peace

That was **THE** most lovely dinner, Alison...marvellous **cassoulet!**

Well, all thanks to **Ben**...I had a hell of a day at school and he did the **lot**, from **soup** to **cheesecake**...**AND** he looked after the kids today...

Aren't we lucky, Wendy, to have such **supportive** husbands... cooking and coping!

Yes, I suppose we ought to enjoy these last, few **golden days** before **HOSTILITIES** break out...

There are **Dark Days** ahead.... the **lights** are going out all over the **Welfare State**...we may never see their like again....

The **Great War** against **Inflation** will advance... cutting down all in its path...**DECIMATING** nursery schools, day care centres for the old...**WIPING OUT** school dinners!

Countless refugees – **TODDLERS, OLD PEOPLE**, starving **SCHOOL CHILDREN**, will straggle the countryside, seeking succour...**AT HOME!**

Working mothers will have toddlers & aged relatives **BILLETED** on them **ALL DAY!** School kids will need hot dinners....

Desperate measures will be taken: **WIVES** will be pulled out of the economic battle-field & sent home for **voluntary service**... able bodied **MEN** will take their place... severe **RATIONING** will ensure just one **MALE** breadwinner per family...

Greater love hath no man than this...that a **MAN** lay down his **JOB** for his **WIFE**...

Whilst their men **BATTLE** Inflation in the market place, the women will keep the **home fires** burning.....until the idea of **dual-career families**, government crèches & paternity leave fade into sad pre-war memories....

With the **HOME FRONT** fully **womanned**, what place will there be for **HOUSE-HUSBANDS?**

They would be cast as **conscientious objectors** by their peers on **Active Service**....white feathers would abound..

Daddy, what did you do in the Great Inflation War?

© Posy Simmonds 1979

The Silent Three

FACTS OF LIFE

But if the social glue is coercion rather than consensus...

...but WHERE exactly do BABIES come from?

ovary
Fallopian tube
uterus

Seeds

Egg

Love

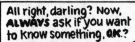

All right, darling? Now, ALWAYS ask if you want to know something, OK.?

Sorry about that, but you can't just FOB them off, can you?

Oh, I KNOW

...you see, Mr TIMMIS loved Mrs TIMMIS so much and Mrs TIMMIS stopped taking her pill...and Mr TIMMIS put a seed in her tummy...and it grew & grew and when it came out it was Keith...SEE!

© Posy Simmonds 1979

Sweet Sorrow

Today, Katya is going to nursery school for the first time....

Dohwanter go....

Come along, darling...

PUSS

OFF we go!

SNIFF!

Oh Katya! Don't cry...

Bwaaaa!

Don't you want to go & find that lovely *slide*? Mm?

Don't you want to play with all those lovely *TRACTORS* & *BIKES* Mrs Jamieson showed us? Eh?

'es.

And the *sand pit*...

...and the *dressing-up box!*

'es

... and the lovely *Wendy House*...

...and all those nice *books* in the *Story Corner!*

& then there are all those lovely things we collected for the *Activity Table*... all those *beans* & *pasta* & *yoghurt pots* & *loo rolls*... are you going to put your pinny on & glue them into a lovely, lovely *collage!?*

Yas!

And Benji'll be there! And *Ned* & *Flora!*

Yes!

And at 11 o'clock you can eat your nice *carrot fingers* & have some lovely *milk*...& then at 12 o'clock I'll come & fetch you, won't I !?

YAS!

Bye bye, darling!

SNIFF!

Oh Angie! Don't cry...

Don't worry - they have such a lovely time....

..there's a *slide*...& a nice *sand pit*..& a lovely *Wendy house*... & a lovely *Activity Table* and you <u>should</u> see the *Story corner!*

...and the dressing up box & the....

Yes

© Posy Simmonds 1980

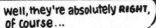

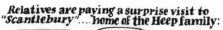

© Posy Simmonds 1981

© Posy Simmonds 1979

The Silent Three

Piggy in the Middle

"...and then the Mummy Piggy gave Daddy Piggy & the 3 little Piggies some nice eggs and bacon for their supper...."

It's **HELL** getting **Benji** off to sleep when he's got a cold, —he wants so many stories....

WOW! that's **HORRIBLE! PIGS** eating **BACON!** I'm not reading this sort of stuff to Benji, Mum!

Go on!

What is this book?

It's one **Grandpa Weber** gave him...it's about a family of **POOR** pigs swindled by some **RICH** pigs.....

THE Poor

"Well done, Pig," said the Mayor.

But it's all right in the end... the **rich** pigs get their **come-uppance**.....

..and the **poor** pigs have the honour to be invited to take **swill** with the Mayor of Saddleback & other **Very Important Pigs!**

"We're proud of you, Pig. You've saved our bacon," said the Mayor, grandly.

...and are thoroughly **patronised** by the look of it! How **nauseating!** Awful **CLASS STEREOTYPES!**

And it's **SO SEXIST!** The mother pig does nothing but slave over the stove in an apron!

Wait a minute!

What's **WRONG** with **STEREOTYPES?** Children need them.

The trouble with **stereo-types** is that people can't let **go** of them as they mature!

But **this** story's got a **MORAL!** Poverty & filth aren't so bad because we lead an **honest & happy** life. You look at page **32** & see how **miserable** the **RICH** pigs are...**MONEY** can't buy everything, you know!

POOR but **HONEST!** What an insidious **MYTH** that is!

You **POOR** pigs have only **one** triumph over the **RICH:**– **Moral Virtue.** Your reward is in heaven, whilst the rich pigs go **hee hee hee** all the way to the bank!

and they lived happily ever after.

Oink!

ZZZ

SHEEP AND GOATS

On a crowded bus:

REPATRIATE the lot of 'em! That's what I say!

MUTTER... MUTTER I mean, I didn't fight in a *World War* to have the whole *bloody* country over run with *blacks* and *Arabs*....

MUTTER... MUTTER... *SWARMS* of filthy <u>REDS</u> everywhere!

And I didn't fight for filthy, long-haired *DOLE-QUEUE SCROUNGERS* neither! They should all be *BIRCHED!*

MUTTER... MUTTER... and bloody *WOMEN* taking our jobs!... MUTTER... ...And *STUDENTS! Red SCUM!* Don't know what *WORK is!!* *BIRCH* the lot of 'em!!

You can't stand there mate... you getting on or off?

OFF!

When the orator has gone:

Oh *DEAR!* What a *CHARMING* man! You'd have to *laugh* if it wasn't so *SAD*, wouldn't you?

Filthy <u>REDS</u> everywhere!

© Posy Simmonds 1980

They're never ever satisfied

No you can't!

Whyee?

...Tamsin...yup...Benji...mm...Sophie......that's it....

PAY HERE

That's £38·40, please...

GOOD GOD!

Tool Kit AGE 3-7

flower press

Oh yes, it is a ve-ry COSTLY time of year, isn't it? But we HAVE to do it, don't we? For the little ones... bless their hearts!

I mean, I'd rather spend Xmas off my POOR FEET with my crochet...... wouldn't you...haahaha?

Mum! Mum! Canive a... MUM!

...But with CHILDREN...we-ll, you have to push the boat out a bit, don't you?

Oh yes

And it's ve-ry pleasant when one's GIFT brings joy to a little face...

...it's such a ve-ry special magic time for them...they look forward to it for SO long!

Sod 'em!

I'm sorry?

Whining little SO & SOS! NEVER content.../ I want I want all the time...

Ungrateful little BEASTS! Money, money, money! That's what's wrong...too much spent on the little.....!

I mean, MY mother never spent £38·40 on ME! I never got given a nice PAINT BOX like this...or nice books!

My sister got a bike for Xmas once...but I never did! I only got a doll's pram...wasn't fair!

I never got given ANYTHING decent... ...just RUBBISH..!!

© Posy Simmonds 1980

SHOWING OFF

While Wendy studies, George is a house-husband.

Today he discovers that the twins need *robin costumes* for their school concert.....

It's **TOMORROW!** *Why* the **hell** didn't you give me this before!?

It's **Manda's** fault! She kept it in her pocket

Didn't!

Well, I can't bother **Mum** now... you know how hard she's got to work for her exam...

But we **GOT** to have costumes! : **WAIL**: Mrs Spedding **SAID!!**

We'd be the only ones without any...

Well...why don't you wear **red** sweaters & **brown** tights...or **something**?

But in his mind George hears the hum of sewing machines...the sound of *mothers* running-up robin outfits.....

In his mind he sees <u>his</u> children the <u>only</u> robins without proper costumes....

...& hears the blame laid at Wendy's door....

Shame about the end two...

Well, *she's* out at work all day... 'got no time for the children..... All wrong, isn't it?

...And in his mind, George knows that true equality isn't just helping with the cooking & washing up..... It's taking on all those little <u>extra</u> worries, which erode a mother's time....

I'll **MAKE** the *bloody* costumes!

Which he does...

...in time for the next day's great event...

My God, those two *robins!* Someone's gone to a lot of trouble

Tsk! some mothers can't have anything else to do all day...

♫ We are wittal wobin wedbweasts... ♫
...hop-ping...hop-ping... ♪

© Posy Simmonds 1980

On the Eighth Day of Christmas my clients sent to me:
8 large Havanas.....7 malted whiskies...6 Rum 'n' Butter Puddings....500 hand-rolled fags...

4 superb Stiltons...3 cases of Claret...2 Madeira cakes & a magnum of Pouilly-Fuissé

The Silent Three ©Posy Simmonds 1978

© Posy Simmonds 1979